W9-BPN-845

Imagine That!

Imagination lets us look at things in new ways.

SCHOLASTIC
LITERACY
PLACE®

Copyright acknowledgments and credits appear on page 152, which constitutes an extension of this copyright page.

Copyright © 1996 by Scholastic Inc.   All rights reserved.   Printed in the U.S.A.
                                             ISBN 0-590-49107-5
                    4 5 6 7 8 9 10   23   02 01 00 99 98 97

Imagine
an Artist's Studio

Imagination lets us look at things in new ways.

3

Can You Imagine?
We use imagination.

Real and Make-Believe

We can tell real from make-believe.

Starring Us

We present stories and pictures.

Trade Books

The following books accompany this *Imagine That!* SourceBook.

Nonfiction
Going Home
by Margaret Wild
illustrated by Wayne Harris

Poetry
Pierre
by Maurice Sendak

Fiction
Jenny's Journey
by Sheila White Samton

Big Books

Fiction
The Snowy Day   Caldecott Honor
by Ezra Jack Keats

Repetitive Story
Mama, Do You Love Me?
by Barbara M. Joosse
illustrated by
Barbara Lavallee

ut I was bored.

So I climbed into the attic.

The attic was empty.

Or was it?

I found a family of mice . . .

18

. . . and a cool, quiet place to rest and think.

I met a spider and we made a web.

I opened windows to other worlds.

I found an old flying machine

and I made it work.

I went out to look for someone

to share what I had found . . .

. . . and I found a friend I could talk to.

My friend and I found a game that could

go on forever, but it was time for dinner.

So I climbed out of the attic, and
told my mother where I'd been all day.
"But we don't have an attic,"
she said.

I guess she doesn't know
about the attic.
　　She hasn't found the ladder.

By Myself

by Eloise Greenfield

When I'm by myself
And I close my eyes
I'm a twin
I'm a dimple in a chin
I'm a room full of toys
I'm a squeaky noise
I'm a gospel song
I'm a gong
I'm a leaf turning red
I'm a loaf of brown bread
I'm a whatever I want to be
An anything I care to be
And when I open my eyes
What I care to be
Is me

35

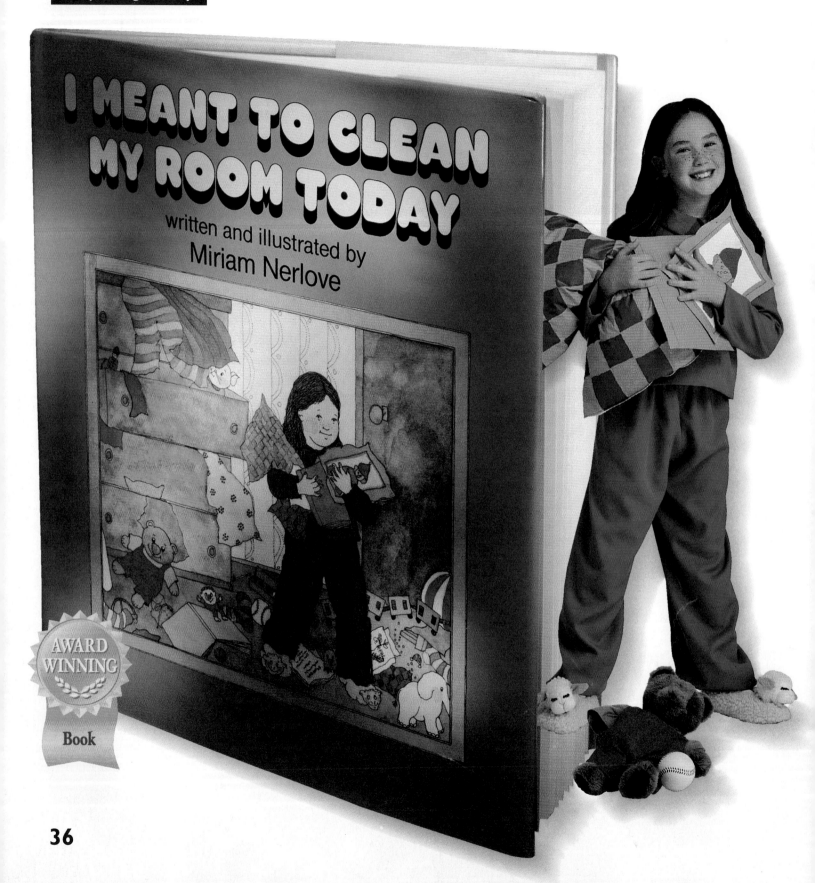

I MEANT TO CLEAN MY ROOM TODAY

written and illustrated by
Miriam Nerlove

AWARD WINNING Book

I meant to clean my room today—

But a big white lion gave a roar,
He would not let me out the door.

A yellow turtle crawled to my bed,
He showed me how to stand on my head.

An orange lamb came to see
If she could roller-skate with me.

And a green kitten romped on the floor,
She chewed my clothes and got stuck in a drawer.

43

A fat blue pig came to get clean,
I filled up the tub—so as not to be mean.

A red giraffe arrived at noon,
He asked me if I'd sing a tune.

And a big beige bunny hopped in for lunch,
We had chocolate ice cream and strawberry punch.

A pink monkey dropped in to play,
He stayed for three hours before going away.

47

And a brown fish asked for a drink,
He made a few puddles and splashed in the sink.

48

A kind gray cow gave a gentle moo,
We read my books and magazines too.

49

And a purple puppy brought me a bone,
We played fetch together—he couldn't play alone.

A rainbow parrot brought me some flowers,
We sat down to visit and gossiped for hours.

I meant to clean my room today,
But other things got in the way.

My Bed

by Franz Brandenberg
Art by Aliki

SOURCE

Ladybug®

Magazine

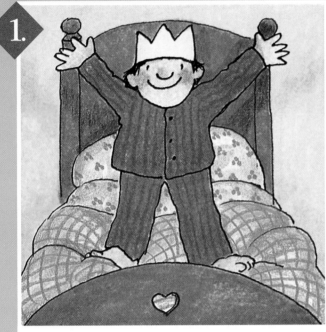

1.

I am the king in my castle.

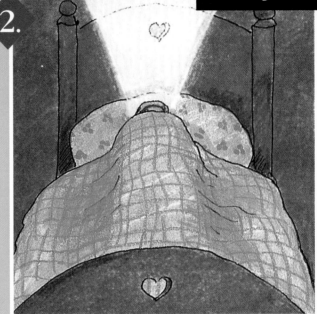

2.

I am a train in a tunnel.

3.

I am an explorer in a cave.

4.

Good night.

Read Together!

Real and Make-Believe

We can tell real from make-believe.

See how Bear dances with the moon. Then meet a boy who wishes on a star.

Learn about the real night sky and what to watch for. Get some tips on how you can watch the night sky.

55

MOONDANCE
FRANK ASCH

SCHOLASTIC

AWARD
WINNING
Author\
Illustrator

One night Bear and Little Bird were sitting outside, looking at the moon.

"You know what I wish?" said Bear. "I wish I could dance with the moon."

"Maybe she'd like to dance with you, too?" chirped Little Bird.

"Silly Bird," chuckled Bear. "The moon is so
special. She wouldn't want to dance with me!"
Just then a cloud drifted in front of the moon.
"What about the clouds?" asked Little Bird.
"Would they dance with you?"
"Mmmmmm...maybe," said Bear.
"Why don't you ask them?"
suggested Little Bird.

"Okay," said Bear and he called to the clouds,
"Clouds, would you come down and dance with me?"
But the clouds stayed up in the sky.
"You see," said Bear. "Even the clouds won't come
down to dance with me!"

Bear and Little Bird watched the sky until bedtime.

Then they said good night and went to sleep.

In the morning Bear looked out his window
and saw fog. He had never seen fog before.
"Oh, my!" he cried. "The clouds came down
to dance with me!"
Bear was so excited! He ran outside
and began to dance with the clouds.

He danced and he danced and he danced.

As the day grew warmer, the fog began to lift.

When the fog was all gone, Bear felt sad.
"Do you think I could have stepped on their toes
or something?" he asked Little Bird.
"Silly Bear," replied Little Bird. "The clouds probably
had some work to do up high in the sky, that's all."

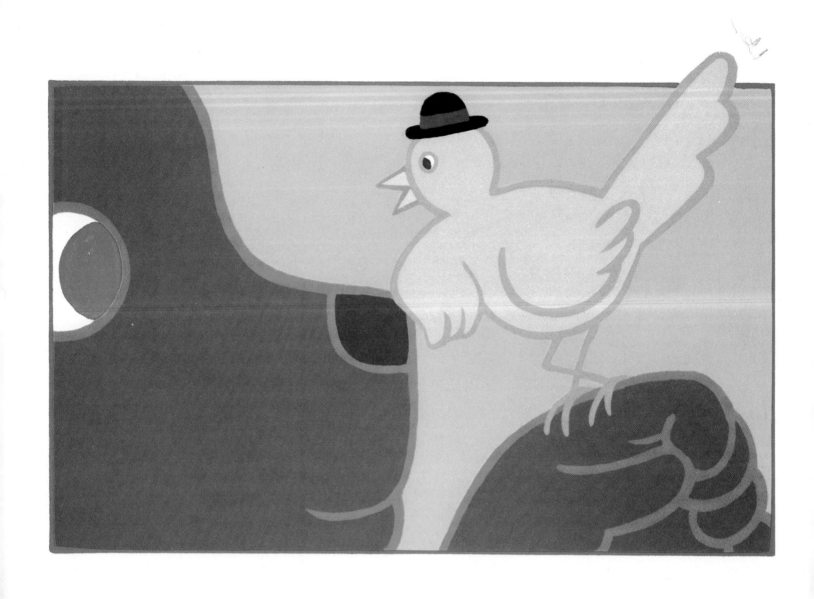

"What kind of work does a cloud do?" asked Bear.
"Clouds make rain," answered Little Bird.
Suddenly Bear had an idea.
"Clouds," he called to the sky, "could you make
some rain for me to dance with?"
Bear heard no answer, not even a rumble of thunder.

"Oh, well," he sighed. "I have my own work to do."
Bear forgot about the clouds.
He went inside and picked up his toys.
He washed the dishes and polished
all the silverware.

When Bear was finished he looked out his window
and saw raindrops falling from the sky.
"Oh, goodie!" cried Bear and he ran outside
and began to dance with the rain!

He danced and he danced and he danced.

After a while the rain stopped.

This time Bear was not sad.
"The rain got hungry and went home
to eat supper, that's all," he said.
Bear was hungry, too.
After eating *his* supper Bear went outside
and waited for the moon to rise.

For a long time Bear gazed at the moon.

"She's so special and I'm just an ordinary bear,"

he thought. Then Bear remembered how special

it made him feel to dance with the clouds and the rain.

"Oh, Moon," he called to the sky,

"will you please come down and dance with me?"

The moon made no reply, but when Bear looked down he saw the moon's reflection in a puddle. "Look, Little Bird!" he cried. "The moon came down to dance with me!"
Bear was so happy! He jumped into the puddle and began to dance with the moon.

He danced and he danced and he danced.

Star Light, Star Bright

★ ★ ★ ★ ★ ★ ★ ★ ★ ★ ★ ★ ★ ★

Illustrated by Scott Nash

Star light, star bright,

First star I see tonight,

I wish I may, I wish I might,

Have the wish I wish tonight.

85

The Night Sky

Written by Alice Pernick

Illustrated by Lisa Desimini

SCHOLASTIC

AWARD WINNING

Illustrator

When the sun sets at the
end of the day, the night sky
begins to twinkle and shine.

There are many things to see
in the night sky.

The moon is the brightest light in the night sky. Sometimes the moon looks full and round.

Sometimes the moon looks thin and curved. It looks different at different times of the month.

Millions of stars twinkle in the night sky. Some look brighter than others. Some look blue and some look white.

Groups of stars that
form patterns in the sky
are called constellations.

Little Dipper

Big Dipper

Some of the brightest points
of light in the night sky are
planets. They look like stars,
but they do not twinkle.

Look at the sky just before
the sun rises. You might see
Venus shining brightly in
the east.

Venus

Comets blaze across the sky. They look like stars with long tails. Comets don't pass by often. If you see a comet, it's your lucky night!

Tips for Watching

the Night Sky

Go out on a night when the
moon is not bright.

Pick a spot where buildings
and trees won't get in the way.

Close your eyes and get used
to the dark.

Open your eyes and look up.
What do you see?

 Read Together!

Starring Us

**We present stories
and pictures.**

See what
happens when
first graders
use their
imaginations
to create a play.

Meet an artist
who helps
children tell
stories through
painted murals.

Read a play
about three
billy goats and
a tough troll
who lives
under a bridge.

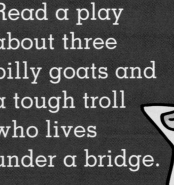

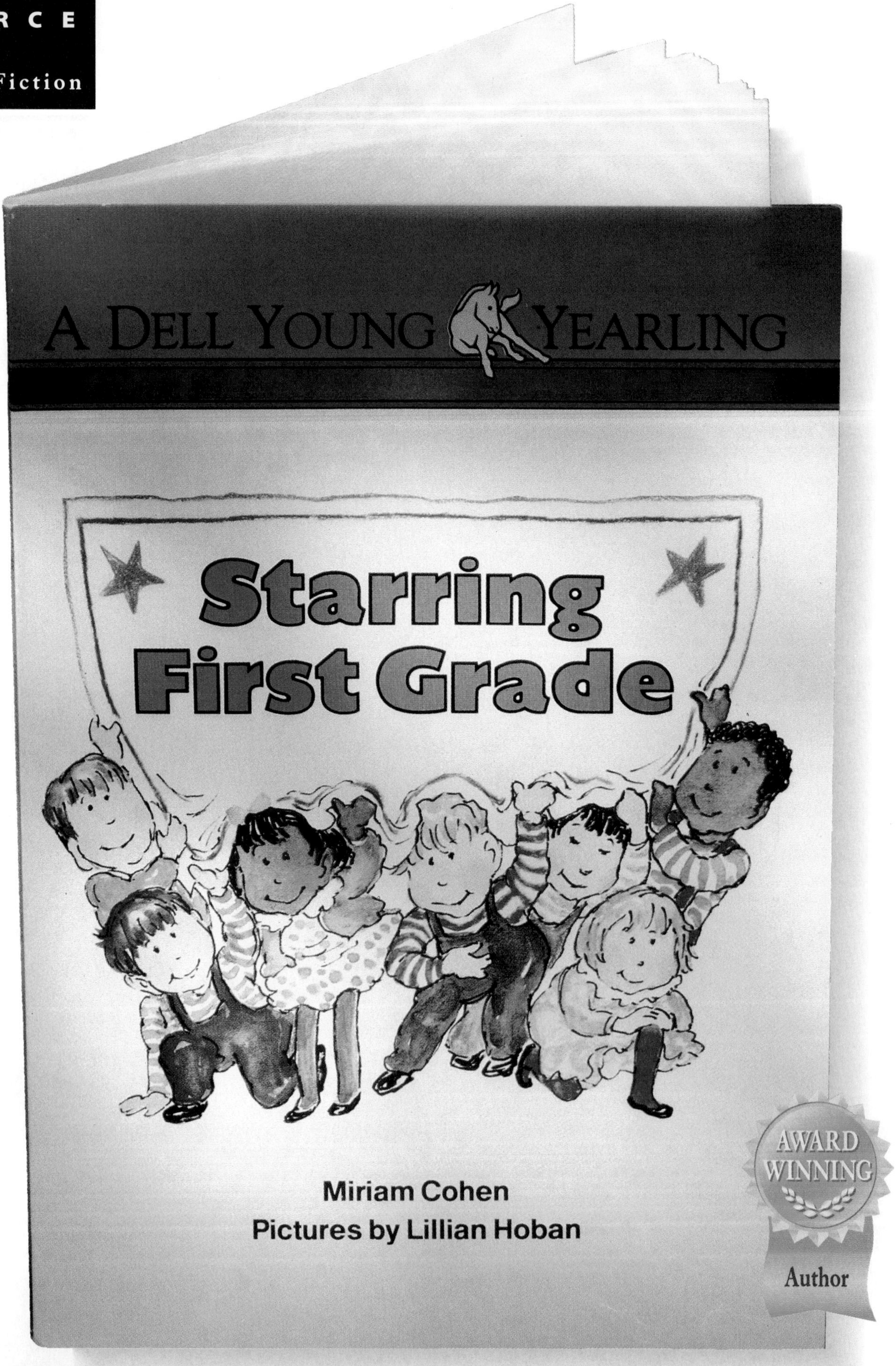

A DELL YOUNG YEARLING

Starring First Grade

Miriam Cohen

Pictures by Lillian Hoban

AWARD WINNING

Author

"First Grade has been asked to put on a play for the school," the teacher said. "Which story should we do?"

Everybody wanted "The Three Billy Goats Gruff,"
especially Danny. He said, "I want to be the
biggest goat that knocks off the troll's ears!"

The teacher picked Paul to be the troll, and
Danny to be the biggest billy goat. She picked
Sara and Margaret to be the other two goats.
"We will have to make up more parts so
everyone can be in the play," she said.

Anna Maria said, "We could have a little
girl snowflake that dances. I'm the only
one that knows how to do it, because
we have snowflakes at my dancing class."

Danny said, "*No* snowflakes!"
But the teacher said Anna Maria could be one.

"We need some trees to stand by the bridge,"
said the teacher. "Jim, you'd make a good,
strong tree. And George, and Louie, and Willy,
and Sammy too."
"Well, somebody has got to be the trees,"
Willy said to Sammy.

But Jim didn't want to be a tree. He wanted to be the troll and make awful faces and scare everybody. He wanted to shout, "Who is going over *my* bridge?"

They began to rehearse. Suddenly,
the tree that was Jim started singing,
"This Land Is Your Land."
"A singing tree! That's stupid,"
Anna Maria said.

Paul was mad. "He's interrupting me!"
he complained.
"It's not like you to act this way, Jim,"
the teacher said.

Jim didn't sing anymore, but he began telling the others what to do. And he kept telling Paul how to be the troll.

"Make him be quiet!" Paul shouted.

Finally, the teacher said, "Jim, go and sit down."

Jim stayed under the cloth and stopped bothering the other actors. But Paul was still mad at him.

After school, Paul said, "You think you're
the boss of everybody!"

He didn't talk to Jim for a whole week,
not even on Friday, the day of the play.

On Friday the school band played as hard
as it could. All the classes marched in.

Soon the auditorium was full of people waiting
for the play to begin. The principal made a long
speech about the play.

Backstage, the teacher whispered,

"Get ready, First Grade. The curtain
is going up in one minute!"

Then the curtain went up. On the bright
stage, the troll waited under the bridge.
The trees were in their places.
The snowflake twirled about near the river.

Sara started across the bridge, Trip-trop,
trip-trop. But Paul didn't say anything. He
just stared at the lights and people.

The teacher whispered, "Who is going across my
bridge?" But Paul just stared and stared. "He's got
stage fright," the people said to each other. It was
awful! Nobody could think what to do.

Then the river lumped up and said, "Somebody is going over your bridge, Mr. Troll. They are going trip-trop, trip-trop."

"Yes!" shouted Paul. "Somebody <u>is</u> going across my bridge and they better watch out! I'll eat them up!" Then they all did their parts perfectly.

At the end, Danny caught the troll
and knocked off his ears.

Everybody cheered for First Grade.

Their teacher pushed Jim and Paul in front
for a bow.
And they grinned and grinned at each other.

📖 Read Together!

William Walsh

Muralist

William Walsh uses his imagination to make murals. Murals are large paintings that tell stories.

Everyone chooses the paint for the mural.

The children make sure the mural looks like their sketch.

130

Everyone has stories to tell.
William Walsh tells his
stories using paints, brushes,
and lots of imagination.

THE THREE BILLY GOATS GRUFF

A Play by Mike Thaler

Illustrated by Vincent Andriani

CAST OF CHARACTERS

Narrator
The person who tells the story

Little Gruff
The little goat who talks in a soft voice

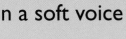

Middle Gruff
The middle-sized goat who talks in a regular voice

Extra Large Gruff
The extra-large goat who talks in a loud voice

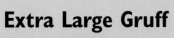

Troll
The bad guy who talks in a mean voice

Sound Effects
The person who makes all the noises

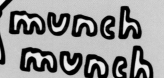

munch munch

Narrator: Once upon a time there were three billy goats Gruff. Little Gruff...

Little Gruff: Hi.

Narrator: Middle Gruff...

Middle Gruff: Hi, hi.

Narrator: And Extra Large Gruff...

Extra Large Gruff: HI, HI, HI!

Narrator: One day they decided to go up the mountain to munch the wonderful things that were growing there.

Little Gruff: Yum.

Middle Gruff: Yum, yum.

Extra Large Gruff: YUM, YUM, YUM!

Narrator: But to get there they had to cross a bridge.

Little Gruff: No problem.

Middle Gruff: No problem.

Extra Large Gruff: NO PROBLEM!

Narrator: But under the bridge lived a mean and hungry Troll.

STOMP

STAMP

STEP

Little Gruff:	Oh!
Middle Gruff:	Oh, oh!
Extra Large Gruff:	NO PROBLEM!
Narrator:	No one could use the bridge without going through his Troll booth.
Troll:	I don't charge a dime. I don't charge a nickel. I'll just eat you up like a crunchy pickle.

136

Little Gruff: Oh!

Middle Gruff: Oh, oh!

Extra Large Gruff: NO PROBLEM!

Narrator: So the three billy goats Gruff set off for the bridge.

Sound Effects: Step! Stamp! STOMP!

Narrator: Little Gruff was the first to arrive.
He started to cross the bridge.

Sound Effects: Step! Step! Step!

Narrator: Out jumped the Troll!

Troll: Who's crossing my bridge?

Little Gruff: It's only me, Little Gruff. I'm on
my way to munch the mountain.

Troll: Well, you have to pay the toll!

Little Gruff: How much is the toll?

Troll: I don't charge a dime.
I don't charge a nickel.
I'll just eat you up
like a crunchy pickle.

STAMP
STAMP

Little Gruff: Oh, don't eat me!
My big brother's coming.
And I have a hunch,
you'll like him better for your lunch.

Troll: Well, okay. I'll wait and eat him.

Narrator: Middle Gruff was the next to arrive. He started to cross the bridge.

Sound Effects: Stamp! Stamp! Stamp!

Troll: Who's crossing my bridge?

Middle Gruff: It's only me, Middle Gruff. I'm on my way to munch the mountain.

STOMP
STOMP

STAMP
STAMP

Troll: Well, you have to pay the toll!

Middle Gruff: How much is the toll?

Troll: I don't charge a dime.
I don't charge a nickel.
I'll just eat you up
like a crunchy pickle.

Middle Gruff: Oh, don't eat me!
My big brother's coming.
And I'm much thinner.
You'll like him better for your dinner.

Troll: Well, okay. I'll wait and eat him.

STEP STEP

Narrator:	Extra Large Gruff was the last to arrive. He started to cross the bridge.
Sound Effects:	STOMP! STOMP! STOMP!
Troll:	Who's crossing my bridge?
Extra Large Gruff:	It's me, Extra Large Gruff. I'm on my way to munch the mountain. What's it to you?
Troll:	Well, you have to pay the toll!
Extra Large Gruff:	No way, Nosey.
Troll:	How did you know my name was Nosey?
Extra Large Gruff:	Listen Nosey, I've got muscles, and my muscles got muscles. And I know kung fu, karate, and goat jitsu.
Troll:	Well, you have to pay the toll anyway.

STOMP!

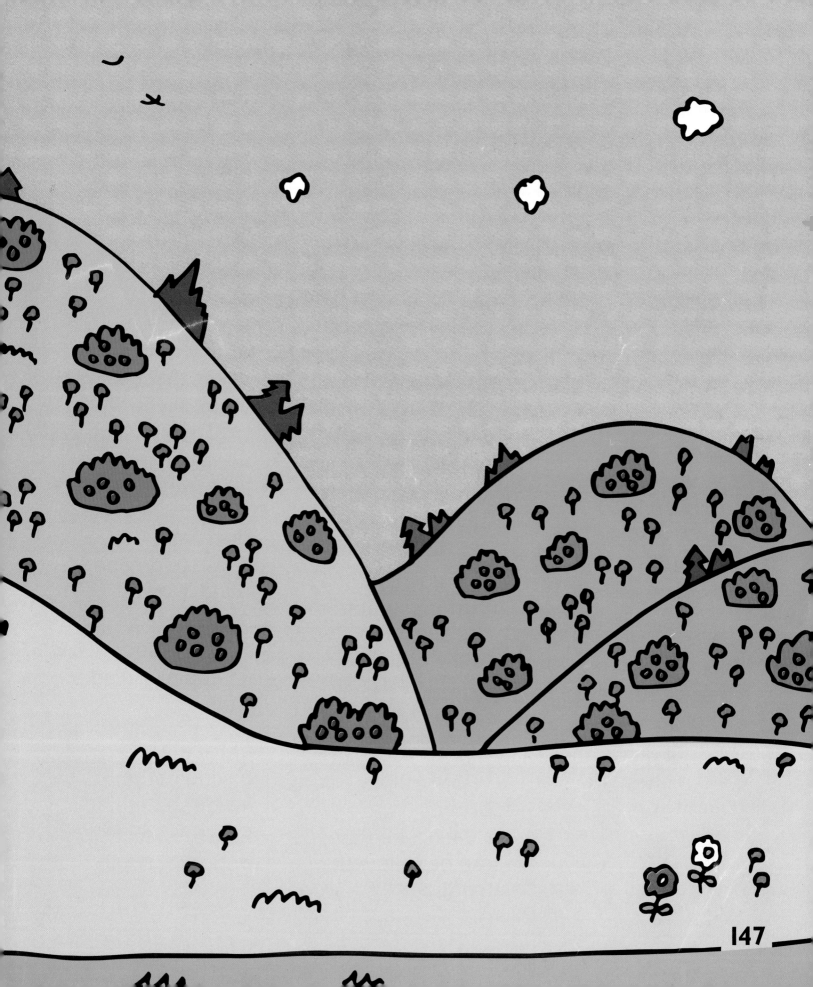

Glossary

actors
people in a play, movie, or TV show

Actors wear costumes, memorize lines, and perform for others.

arrive
to come to a place

The plane will **arrive** at noon.

attic
the space or room below the roof of a house

We put old clothes and pictures in our **attic.**

clouds

bridge
something that is built for people to get across water

Cars go over the **bridge** to get from one side of the water to the other.

bright
filled with light

A spotlight is a **bright** light.

brown
a dark color that can be yellowish or reddish

Dirt is **brown.**

clouds
large bodies, made of tiny drops of water, that float high in the sky

Use your imagination to find shapes in **clouds.**

decided
chose to do one thing instead of another

Jack **decided** to have an apple instead of a pear.

empty
having nothing inside something

Empty is the opposite of full.

giraffe
a large animal that has a long neck, long legs, and a spotted coat

The **giraffe** is the tallest animal on earth.

giraffe

ladder
a set of steps used for climbing that can be moved from one place to another

Mom used the **ladder** to paint the ceiling.

magazines
collections of stories, articles, and pictures that are usually published monthly

Sara reads **magazines** with jokes.

moon
the heavenly body that moves around the Earth

It takes 29 1/2 days for the **moon** to move completely around the Earth.

planets
the nine heavenly bodies that move around the sun

The Earth is one of the **planets**.

problem
something that is difficult to deal with or hard to understand

When I have a **problem**, I sometimes ask my dad for help.

sky
the space or air above the Earth

Sometimes you can see the moon in the **sky** at night.

stars
large, faraway bodies that look like small bright lights, and can usually be seen in the night sky

From the Earth, **stars** look small and white.

teacher
a person who helps people learn things

My **teacher** knows a lot about numbers.

thunder
the loud sound in the sky that comes after lightning

When my dog hears **thunder**, he hides under the bed.

whispered
spoke in a quiet voice

Susan **whispered** in the library.

Authors and Illustrators

Frank Asch   pages 56-84

When Frank Asch was a little boy, he liked to explore nature. He still does. Even though he's grown up, he likes to look at the moon—just like Bear! He has written over 40 books, many of them about Bear and his friends. These include *Mooncake* and *Bear Shadow*.

Miriam Cohen   pages 102-129

Miriam Cohen remembers a lot of the things that happened to her three children when they were in kindergarten and first grade. These memories help her write stories that seem both real and funny. She has written many books about Ann Marie, Jim, and the other kids in their class, such as *First Grade Takes a Test* and *When Will I Read?*

Read Together!

Eloise Greenfield page 35

Eloise Greenfield is a famous author who has won many awards. The first thing she wrote was not a story. It was a little rhyme. She had so much fun writing rhymes and songs that she kept on writing. *My Daddy and I* and *Under the Sunday Tree* are just two of the many books she has written.

Satoshi Kitamura
pages 10-34

Satoshi Kitamura grew up in Tokyo, Japan. Now he lives and works in London, England. He says he has fun working on picture books because he likes all the ways words and pictures can come together. Satoshi Kitamura drew the pictures for *From Acorn to Zoo*, and he wrote and illustrated *When Sheep Cannot Sleep.*

151

Acknowledgments

Grateful acknowledgment is made to the following sources for permission to reprint from previously published material. The publisher has made diligent efforts to trace the ownership of all copyrighted material in this volume and believes that all necessary permissions have been secured. If any errors or omissions have inadvertently been made, proper corrections will gladly be made in future editions.

Cover: From IN THE ATTIC by Hiawyn Oram, illustrated by Satoshi Kitamura. Cover illustration © 1984 by Satoshi Kitamura. Reprinted by arrangement with Henry Holt and Co.

Interior: "In the Attic" from IN THE ATTIC by Hiawyn Oram, illustrated by Satoshi Kitamura. Text copyright © 1984 by Hiawyn Oram, illustrations copyright © 1984 by Satoshi Kitamura. Reprinted by arrangement with Henry Holt and Co.

"By Myself" from HONEY, I LOVE by Eloise Greenfield. Text copyright © 1978 by Eloise Greenfield. Reprinted by permission of HarperCollins Publishers.

"I Meant to Clean My Room Today" from I MEANT TO CLEAN MY ROOM TODAY by Miriam Nerlove. Copyright © 1988 by Miriam Nerlove. This edition is reprinted by arrangement with Margaret K. McElderry Books, Simon & Schuster Children's Publishing Division.

"My Bed" by Franz Brandenberg, illustrated by Aliki. Text copyright © 1992 by Franz Brandenberg. Illustrations copyright © 1992 by Aliki Brandenberg. Taken from HOME, edited by Michael J. Rosen. Copyright © 1992 by HarperCollins Publishers. Reprinted by permission of Share Our Strength. Logo reprinted by permission of *Ladybug* magazine, copyright © 1994 by Carus Publishing Company.

"Moondance" from MOONDANCE by Frank Asch. Copyright © 1993 by Frank Asch. Reprinted by permission of Scholastic Inc.

"The Night Sky" from THE NIGHT SKY by Alice Pernick, illustrated by Lisa Desimini. Copyright © 1994 by Scholastic Inc.

"Starring First Grade" from STARRING FIRST GRADE by Miriam Cohen, illustrated by Lillian Hoban. Text copyright © 1985 by Miriam Cohen. Cover and internal illustrations copyright © 1985 by Lillian Hoban. Reprinted by permission of Greenwillow Books, a division of William Morrow & Company, Inc. Cover used with permission of Delacorte Press, a division of Bantam Doubleday Dell Publishing Group, Inc.

THE THREE BILLY GOATS GRUFF by Mike Thaler, illustrated by Vincent Andriani. Copyright © 1996 by Scholastic Inc.

Cover from GOING HOME by Margaret Wild, illustrated by Wayne Harris. Illustration copyright © 1993 by Wayne Harris. Published by Scholastic Inc.

Cover from JENNY'S JOURNEY by Sheila White Samton. Illustration copyright © 1991 by Sheila Samton. Published by Viking Penguin, a division of Penguin Books USA Inc.

Cover from MAMA, DO YOU LOVE ME? by Barbara M. Joosse, illustrated by Barbara Lavallee. Illustration copyright © 1991 by Barbara Lavallee. Published by Chronicle Books.

Cover from PIERRE: A CAUTIONARY TALE by Maurice Sendak. Illustration copyright © 1962 by Maurice Sendak. Published by HarperCollins Children's Books, a division of HarperCollins Publishers.

Cover from THE SNOWY DAY by Ezra Jack Keats. Illustration copyright © 1962 by Ezra Jack Keats. Published by Viking Penguin, a division of Penguin Books USA Inc.

Photography and Illustration Credits

Selection Opener Photographs by David S. Waitz Photography/Alleycat Design, Inc.

Photos: p. 2 c: tl: © Merry Alpern for Scholastic Inc. p. 2 bl: © Merry Alpern for Scholastic Inc. pp. 2-3 c: © Merry Alpern for Scholastic Inc. p. 3 br: © Merry Alpern for Scholastic Inc. p. 35: © Halley Ganges for Scholastic Inc. p. 130 cl, bl: Merry Alpern for Scholastic Inc. p. 131 c: © Merry Alpern for Scholastic Inc. p. 148 tc: © Bill Losh/FPG International Corp. p. 149 tl: © Chris Michaels/FPG International Corp. p. 150 bl: © Courtesy of Holiday House.

Illustrations: pp. 2-3: Jackie Snider; pp. 8-9: Shelly Dieterichs; p. 35: Beatrice Brooks; pp. 54-55: Shelly Dieterichs; p. 85: Scott Nash; pp. 100-101: Shelly Dieterichs.